Sophia Saves the Earth

A Story of Gaylord Nelson, Founder of Earth Day

Written by Curt Casetta
www.CasettaKids.com

Layout by Michael Nicloy and Curt Casetta

Edited by Marla McKenna

ISBN: 978-1945907555

Published by Nico 11 Publishing & Design | Mukwonago, Wisconsin
www.nico11publishing.com

Be well read.

Quantity orders may be requested by contacting the publisher: mike@nico11publishing.com

Printed in The United States of America

To my wife, Jodi,

my mom, Joan,

and to the Father of Earth Day, Gaylord Nelson.

Foreword

by Tia Nelson

Managing Director, Climate, at Outrider.org,
daughter of Earth Day founder, U.S. Senator Gaylord Nelson.

On the very first Earth Day, my father said, "Our goal is not just an environment of clean air and water and scenic beauty. The objective is an environment of decency, quality and mutual respect for all other human beings and all other living creatures."

Fifty years later, we still strive for that goal. As the risks to ourselves and the planet from climate change grow we must remember that each of us, especially today's youth, has the power to make a difference, just like the first Earth Day 50 years ago.

Every child that reads a book such as this is another hope for a positive future.

As my father often said, "The job's not done."

Follow Tia on Twitter: @tialeenelson

I'm Sophia.
I'm going to my grandma's house.
She wants us to plant a tree today.
Seriously? Like, we need another tree?
I mean, over there's a tree, and there's a tree, and—HEY!—under that candy wrapper, there's a quarter!
It's old, from 1961.
MILK
CHOCOLATE

An eagle is on the back.

I'm about to put it in my pocket and something really weird happens. The eagle shakes his head.

His wings kind of flutter.

Suddenly...

...this eagle flies out and sits on top of the park bench.

"So," he says, "what are you doing?"

I gasp. "Are you talking to me?"

He nods. "What are you doing?"

"Um...talking to an eagle?"

The eagle shakes his head.

"No. I mean, did you see that candy wrapper?"

"Yeah. I moved it to get the quarter."

"And you didn't throw it away because..."

"Because it's not my garbage."

The eagle's feathers ruffle a little.

He asks, "Do you know what today is?"

"Yeah. It's Wednesday."

"Not just Wednesday!" he screeches with a big smile.

"Wednesday, April 22!

IT'S EARTH DAY!"

"Big deal."

"Yes, it is!" he says. "Let me tell you a story."

"I gotta go..."

"It's called *Sophia Saves the Earth*."

MILK
CHOCOLATE

"Really? *Sophia Saves the Earth?*
From what? Zombies? Aliens?
Giant bugs?"

The eagle chuckles.

"Well," he says, "it starts with a kid named Gaylord
Nelson. Except when he was growing up,
everyone called him 'Happy.'"

Happy? I'm thinking,
...a few people call me grumpy...

"Happy likes nature and being outside,"
he continues."He's just a kid. Maybe a lot like you."

MILK

The eagle hops down.

He puts a big, old wing around my shoulders.

"Without Happy—I mean, Gaylord—Earth wouldn't be as nice or as clean."

"What is he, a garbage collector?"

The eagle rolls his eyes.

"Uh, no. Gaylord grew up to pass laws that help the Earth. And even after helping Earth a lot, he said, 'There's a lot more to be done.'"

"I really gotta go..."

He spreads his wings.

"Hop on—we'll travel through time,
and I'll tell you the story. It won't take long."

Riding an eagle? Travelling through time?

Hmmmm...maybe planting Grandma's tree
can wait a little longer.

"Hold on—gently, please."

I climb aboard and grab some feathers.

"GENTLY, PLEASE!" he screeches.

"Oops, sorry."

Then...

MILK
CHOCOLATE

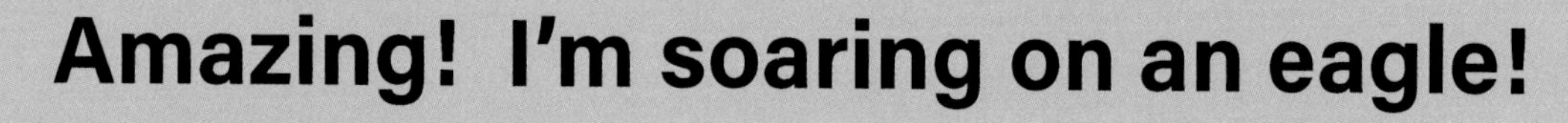

Amazing! I’m soaring on an eagle!

"You saw my coin. I've been around since 1961."

We fly over a shoreline.

"This is 1961."

Waves splash against cliffs and islands.

"Beautiful," I say.

"This is when Gaylord really started saving natural places so people could always enjoy them. Even today, this place looks the same."

"So, everything's the same? Big deal."

"It is! And Gaylord helped change things that needed to be changed. HOLD ON!"

I grab the feathers.

"GENTLY, PLEASE!"

Off we go...

...I notice a city with old-style cars spitting out smoke.

“As there were more cars, there was less fresh air,” he says.

It’s hazy. The sun looks like a flashlight through a blanket.

“This is how it used to be.”

“Horrible,” I cough.

“Gaylord helped pass laws cutting down harmful smoke. HOLD ON!”

The eagle turns a wide circle.

“This is how it looks today.”

Below is the same city.

I see streets and cars without the smoke.

“Wow, awesome.”

“But there were other problems,” he says.

“HOLD ON!”

Soon, we're above a lake.
Things are floating and covering the beaches.

"Water was ruined because people kept
dumping chemicals into it," he tells me.
"It used to look like this."

"OOOH, IT STINKS!" I yell.

I look closer. Those are fish! Hundreds of dead fish!
The smell is terrible, but seeing this is even worse.

"Gaylord helped make rules to
keep water cleaner," he says.
"HOLD ON!"

We turn again.

Now the lake has clear water and clean beaches.

"Okay, so Gaylord helped make the air and water cleaner. When do we get to the Sophia part?" I ask.

"It's coming. Just a couple more stops."

"Let me guess," I shout,

"HOLD ON!"

We soar above another beach. It's black and shiny.

"Gaylord saw that oil spills like this one hurt the Earth. He wanted people thinking about Earth one special day each year," the eagle says.

"Let's stop in and see how people are doing that back here in 1970."

We zoom down to a vacant field.
I help a bunch of kids pick up trash.
Someone calls me over to plant a tree.

I'm patting down the dirt around the sapling,
and I stop. Thoughts are exploding in my brain.

A special day for the Earth...
people picking up garbage...
planting trees...

"I got it!" I yell...

"...today is Earth Day!"
My thoughts spill out, "And that's why you're here...and that's why Grandma wants us to plant a tree..."

The eagle nods.

"And Gaylord started it, didn't he?"

"He sure did," the eagle smiles. "Way back here in 1970."

"And Earth still needs help, doesn't it?" I ask.
"Like Gaylord said, there's a lot more to be done."

"That's right, Sophia."

I brush the dirt off my knees.
I climb aboard the eagle's back and hold on—gently.

"Are you ready to go home, Sophia?"

"I guess so, but, eagle," I ask, "why do you care so much?"

He slows down by some treetops.

"Here's an eagle's nest of the past," he says.

"The eggs are broken," I notice.

"A chemical got in our food. It made our eggshells weak.
They cracked before they were ready to hatch."

I'm afraid to ask. "Did the baby eagles die?"

"They did." A teardrop crosses the eagle's cheek.
"Gaylord got people to stop using that chemical.
Without Gaylord..." his voice trails off.

"...the eagles would be extinct," I whisper.

He nods.

"Where now, friend?" I ask.

"Home, Sophia. My story's almost finished."

"But, eagle, this isn't really
Sophia Saves the Earth, is it?
It's *Gaylord Nelson Saves the Earth*."

"Yes," says the eagle with a wink,
"but now it's up to you...

...It's *your* turn to save the Earth."
All of the sudden...

...I'm back where I started, holding the old quarter.
The candy wrapper is at my feet.
I hear the words, "There's a lot more to be done."

I pick up the candy wrapper.
I head off to help Grandma plant her tree.

But I stop.

I put the quarter back for the
next kid who comes along.

If I'm going to save the Earth,

I'm gonna need some help.

Timeline of Gaylord Nelson

June 4, 1916	Gaylord "Happy" Nelson is born in Clear Lake, Wisconsin
1948-1959	Serves as Wisconsin State Senator
1959-1963	Serves as Wisconsin Governor
1963-1981	Serves as United States Senator from Wisconsin
1963	US Clean Air Act becomes law (to keep air cleaner)
1964	Wilderness Act becomes law (to keep natural areas from being destroyed)
1966	Introduces a law to stop (ban) DDT, the pesticide that damages eggshells
1968	National Trails System Act passes (to form and protect trails such as the Appalachian Trail and the Ice Age Trail)

April 22, 1970	**First Earth Day**
1970	**US Environmental Protection Agency forms (to keep the environment clean)**
1972	**US Clean Water Act becomes law (to keep water cleaner)**
1972	**DDT is banned (eagles are saved)**
1981	**Becomes a Board Member of The Wilderness Society**
1995	**Receives the Presidential Medal of Freedom**
July 3, 2005	**Gaylord Nelson dies in Maryland**

Gaylord Nelson sponsored or provided important support to pass all of these national environmental laws.

RUSSELL B. LONG, LA., CHAIRMAN

CLINTON P. ANDERSON, N. MEX.	WALLACE F. BENNETT, UTAH
HERMAN E. TALMADGE, GA.	CARL T. CURTIS, NEBR.
VANCE HARTKE, IND.	JACK MILLER, IOWA
J. W. FULBRIGHT, ARK.	LEN B. JORDAN, IDAHO
ABRAHAM RIBICOFF, CONN.	PAUL J. FANNIN, ARIZ.
FRED R. HARRIS, OKLA.	CLIFFORD P. HANSEN, WYO.
HARRY F. BYRD, JR., VA.	ROBERT P. GRIFFIN, MICH.
GAYLORD NELSON, WIS.	

TOM VAIL, CHIEF COUNSEL

United States Senate

COMMITTEE ON FINANCE

WASHINGTON, D.C. 20510

March 18, 1971

Mr. Curt Casetta
3250 West Rochelle Avenue
Milwaukee, Wisconsin 53209

Dear Curt:

Thank you for your letter and your questions about my work as a United States Senator.

I was born in Clear Lake, Wisconsin which is in the northwestern part of the state on June 4, 1916, and when I was a little boy I listened to Senator Robert Marion LaFollete deliver a campaign speech in northern Wisconsin. I remember how well he spoke, and how much he impressed me. From that time, I wanted to follow in his footsteps.

I really entered politics right after I was discharged from the Army in the mid 1940's when I ran for the State Assembly from Clear Lake, and lost. After that, I moved to Madison and was lucky to be elected to the State Legislature where I served until I was elected Governor in 1958. In 1962, I was elected to the U.S. Senate where I have served ever since.

Now that I am a United States Senator, I am trying to do the best job possible. My plans for the future are to involve myself even more deeply in the problems of our environment, and the other matters of national importance with which we deal in the Senate.

I hope that my answers have been of help to you, and that you will contact me again whenever I can be of assistance.

Sincerely,

Gaylord Nelson

GAYLORD NELSON
U.S. Senator

Gaylord Nelson sent this letter about his life to the author (then 10 years old) to help with his school report in the year following the first Earth Day.

Do something to "Save the Earth" and wear this badge proudly!

Share it at www.CasettaKids.com

Made in the USA
Middletown, DE
23 March 2020